Mastering 11+
English & Verbal Reasoning
Practice Book 3

ashkraft
EDUCATIONAL

Mastering 11+ © 2014 ashkraft educational

This page is intentionally left blank

Mastering 11+
English & Verbal Reasoning
Practice Book 3

ISBN-13: 978-1-910678-02-2

9 781910 678022

DEDICATION

To all children preparing for the eleven plus exams and
the parents who want nothing but the best for their kids.

"Before anything else,
preparation is the key success"

Alexander Graham Bell

Table of Contents

ODD WORDS

"An investment in knowledge
pays the best interest"
Benjamin Franklin

EXERCISE 1: Odd Words Out

Instructions: Select TWO words from each group of words that do NOT belong to that group. You are expected to complete this exercise within 5 minutes.

1	A ▭ Sympathy	B ▭ Synergy	C ▭ Empathy	D ▭ Consideration	E ▭ Synthetic	F ▭ Compassion

2	A ▭ Board	B ▭ Panel	C ▭ Plank	D ▭ Beam	E ▭ Chalk	F ▭ Pen

3	A ▭ Faraway	B ▭ Dream	C ▭ Imagination	D ▭ Distant	E ▭ Secluded	F ▭ Remote

4	A ▭ Thunder	B ▭ Rumble	C ▭ Roar	D ▭ Boom	E ▭ Zoom	F ▭ Whizz

5	A ▭ Endangered	B ▭ Threatened	C ▭ Rear	D ▭ Vanishing	E ▭ Rare	F ▭ Risky

6	A ▭ Credit	B ▭ Acclaim	C ▭ Praise	D ▭ Debit	E ▭ Dispute	F ▭ Recognition

7	A ▭ Internal	B ▭ Interval	C ▭ Break	D ▭ Recess	E ▭ Intermission	F ▭ Interior

8	A ☐ Royal	B ☐ Imperial	C ☐ Decimal	D ☐ Stately	E ☐ Regal	F ☐ Excel

9	A ☐ Autonomous	B ☐ Separate	C ☐ Free	D ☐ Independent	E ☐ Reliant	F ☐ Dependent

10	A ☐ Spain	B ☐ Portugal	C ☐ Brazil	D ☐ Italy	E ☐ Germany	F ☐ France

11	A ☐ Lemon	B ☐ Tomato	C ☐ Apple	D ☐ Orange	E ☐ Grapes	F ☐ Banana

12	A ☐ Simmer	B ☐ Seethe	C ☐ Chain	D ☐ Fume	E ☐ Rage	F ☐ Summer

13	A ☐ Embargo	B ☐ Permit	C ☐ Restraint	D ☐ Sanction	E ☐ Ban	F ☐ Restriction

14	A ☐ Grimace	B ☐ Scowl	C ☐ Glare	D ☐ Frown	E ☐ Freeze	F ☐ Temperate

15	A ☐ Bond	B ☐ Pledge	C ☐ Premise	D ☐ Oath	E ☐ Promise	F ☐ Idea

Mastering 11+ ™ / English & VR – Book THREE / ashkraft educational

EXERCISE 2: Odd Words Out

Instructions: Select TWO words from each group of words that do NOT belong to that group. You are expected to complete this exercise within 5 minutes.

	A	B	C	D	E	F
1	Basic	Evidence	Dispensable	Elementary	Essential	Necessary
2	Allowed	Aloud	Approved	Proven	Authorised	Legitimate
3	Ascent	Accent	Assert	Elevation	Climb	Rise
4	Ancestor	Forebear	Forbear	Predecessor	Abstain	Forefather
5	Strength	Farce	Shambles	Potency	Might	Power
6	Refuge	Shelter	Protection	Asylum	Steadfast	Regular
7	Rain	Control	Reign	Persuade	Downpour	Influence

8	A	B	C	D	E	F
	Timid	Shy	Bashful	Bash	Party	Modest

9	A	B	C	D	E	F
	Strange	Bizarre	Stronger	Eccentric	Odd	Even

10	A	B	C	D	E	F
	Owl	Growl	Thunder	Roar	Rumble	Scowl

11	A	B	C	D	E	F
	Concern	Comfort	Solace	Support	Relief	Southern

12	A	B	C	D	E	F
	Love	Loathe	Detest	Respect	Despise	Hate

13	A	B	C	D	E	F
	Clever	Nifty	Clean	Shrewd	Keen	Sparkling

14	A	B	C	D	E	F
	Cuff	Scuffle	Brawl	Fracas	Restraint	Fray

15	A	B	C	D	E	F
	Surrender	Offensive	Submission	Aggressive	Attacking	Belligerent

Mastering 11+ ™ / English & VR – Book THREE / ashkraft educational

EXERCISE 3: Odd Words Out

Instructions: Select TWO words from each group of words that do NOT belong to that group. You are expected to complete this exercise within 5 minutes.

1
A	B	C	D	E	F
Captive	Capital	Enslaved	Captivate	Confined	Imprisoned

2
A	B	C	D	E	F
Liberal	Generous	Lavish	Meagre	Paltry	Princely

3
A	B	C	D	E	F
Lively	Responsive	Zoom	Sonic	Swift	Nimble

4
A	B	C	D	E	F
Personal	Personnel	Employees	Workers	Private	Recruits

5
A	B	C	D	E	F
Swamp	Marsh	Wetland	Mire	Sink	Drench

6
A	B	C	D	E	F
Raven	Gulp	Gobble	Belt	Pulp	Scoff

7
A	B	C	D	E	F
Plate	Bowl	Saucer	Cup	Spoon	Fork

8	A Encrypt	B Decode	C Encode	D Scramble	E Decrypt	F Code

9	A Solution	B Problem	C Issue	D Answer	E Resolution	F Key

10	A Thaw	B Soften	C Melt	D Freeze	E Dissolve	F Stay

11	A Deject	B Desire	C Dismay	D Dampen	E Discourage	F Dissect

12	A Authentic	B Genuine	C Realistic	D Reliable	E Relevant	F Authority

13	A Riot	B Relax	C Right	D Revolt	E Rebellion	F Unrest

14	A Parallel	B Perpendicular	C Diagonal	D Equivalent	E Similar	F Comparable

15	A Meagre	B Merge	C Bend	D Unite	E Fuse	F Blend

Mastering 11+ ™ / English & VR – Book THREE / ashkraft educational

EXERCISE 4: Odd Words Out

Instructions: Select TWO words from each group of words that do NOT belong to that group. You are expected to complete this exercise within 5 minutes.

	A	B	C	D	E	F
1	Vulnerable	Weak	Venerable	Revered	Helpless	Exposed
2	Deliberate	Planned	Chance	Unplanned	Random	Accidental
3	Driver	Agent	Mediator	Negotiator	Manager	Vehicle
4	Stray	Digress	Digest	Deviate	Swerve	Arrive
5	Tranquil	Serene	Piece	Calm	Peaceful	Quite
6	Benefit	Injury	Advantage	Use	Welfare	Harm
7	Ample	Plenty	Scarce	Inadequate	Liberal	Copious

8	**A** Witless	**B** Serious	**C** Silly	**D** Clueless	**E** Foolish	**F** Sensible

9	**A** Alien	**B** Ally	**C** Friend	**D** Partner	**E** Assistant	**F** Guest

10	**A** Terminal	**B** Lethal	**C** Station	**D** Depot	**E** Terminus	**F** Fatal

11	**A** Tardy	**B** Tidy	**C** Late	**D** Slow	**E** Punctual	**F** Behind

12	**A** Swift	**B** Change	**C** Shift	**D** Tangle	**E** Switch	**F** Toggle

13	**A** Wool	**B** Flee	**C** Cotton	**D** Fleas	**E** Silk	**F** Denim

14	**A** Nibble	**B** Bite	**C** Nimble	**D** Chew	**E** Spec	**F** Particular

15	**A** Sequence	**B** Serious	**C** Order	**D** Arrangement	**E** Structure	**F** Amber

Mastering 11+ ™ / English & VR – Book THREE / ashkraft educational

EXERCISE 5: Odd Words Out

Instructions: Select TWO words from each group of words that do NOT belong to that group. You are expected to complete this exercise within 5 minutes.

1

A	B	C	D	E	F
Dismal	Dismiss	Miserable	Bleak	Grim	Marvel

2

A	B	C	D	E	F
Amass	Accumulate	Connect	Content	Collect	Accrue

3

A	B	C	D	E	F
Supple	Agile	Elastic	Limber	Rubber	Rigid

4

A	B	C	D	E	F
Clarify	Distort	Alter	Deform	Disfigure	Lead

5

A	B	C	D	E	F
Chuckle	Juggle	Giggle	Snigger	Simple	Laugh

6

A	B	C	D	E	F
Jubilee	Festivity	Fortnightly	Annual	Celebration	Anniversary

7

A	B	C	D	E	F
Explicit	Elusive	Vague	Unclear	Definite	Indistinct

8	A	B	C	D	E	F
	Gnaw	Trouble	Worry	Bother	Concert	Change

9	A	B	C	D	E	F
	Silver	Quiver	Quick	Quake	Tremble	Shiver

10	A	B	C	D	E	F
	Infest	Intersect	Infect	Plague	Infiltrate	Filter

11	A	B	C	D	E	F
	Peasant	Humid	Temperate	Clement	Mild	Moderate

12	A	B	C	D	E	F
	Victor	Dud	Champ	Failure	Conqueror	Winner

13	A	B	C	D	E	F
	Extent	Spend	Abuse	Use	Waste	Expend

14	A	B	C	D	E	F
	Charm	Lure	Attraction	Temptation	Harm	Repulsion

15	A	B	C	D	E	F
	Bland	Tasty	Plain	Mild	Weak	Spicy

Mastering 11+ ™ / English & VR – Book THREE / ashkraft educational

EXERCISE 6: Odd Words Out

Instructions: Select TWO words from each group of words that do NOT belong to that group. You are expected to complete this exercise within 5 minutes.

	A	B	C	D	E	F
1	Tense	Relaxed	Laidback	Comfortable	Carefree	Uptight
2	Paltry	Measly	Trifling	Substantial	Mean	Considerable
3	January	March	June	July	August	September
4	Freedom	Careless	Liberty	Autonomy	Diplomatic	Independence
5	Coarse	Rough	Crude	Even	Harsh	Smooth
6	Mint	Pristine	Blemished	Used	Perfect	Untarnished
7	Direct	Hidden	Implicit	Implied	Inherent	Inherited

8	A ▭ Sun	B ▭ Jupiter	C ▭ Mars	D ▭ Venus	E ▭ Earth	F ▭ Moon

9	A ▭ Clan	B ▭ Family	C ▭ Tribe	D ▭ Band	E ▭ Child	F ▭ Baby

10	A ▭ Invention	B ▭ Innovation	C ▭ Discovery	D ▭ Creation	E ▭ Stagnate	F ▭ Avail

11	A ▭ Flock	B ▭ Horde	C ▭ Major	D ▭ Drove	E ▭ Pack	F ▭ Minor

12	A ▭ Subdued	B ▭ Elated	C ▭ Quiet	D ▭ Serious	E ▭ Excited	F ▭ Downcast

13	A ▭ Dynamic	B ▭ Fixed	C ▭ Static	D ▭ Variable	E ▭ Constant	F ▭ Inactive

14	A ▭ Adorn	B ▭ Beautify	C ▭ Decorate	D ▭ Shed	E ▭ Peel	F ▭ Enhance

15	A ▭ Neglect	B ▭ Overlook	C ▭ Sustain	D ▭ Maintain	E ▭ Support	F ▭ Provide

Mastering 11+ ™ / English & VR – Book THREE / ashkraft educational

EXERCISE 7: Odd Words Out

Instructions: Select TWO words from each group of words that do NOT belong to that group. You are expected to complete this exercise within 5 minutes.

	A	B	C	D	E	F
1	Accord	Abandon	Desert	Dessert	Forsake	Discard
2	Bulk	Coil	Foil	Frustrate	Halt	Balk
3	Reduce	Lower	Demote	Relate	Relegate	Promote
4	Confine	Coffin	Restrict	Limit	Narrow	Wide
5	Authority	Cruel	Power	Supremacy	Promise	Rule
6	Trusting	Naïve	Suspicious	Wary	Innocent	Gullible
7	Unusual	Innovative	Traditional	Habitual	Accepted	Conventional

8	A Stage	B Period	C Interim	D Phase	E Temporary	F Segment

9	A Uncertain	B Persistent	C Resolute	D Dedicated	E Shaky	F Steadfast

10	A Stern	B Agreeable	C Strict	D Firm	E Unyielding	F Lenient

11	A Unused	B Engaged	C Vacant	D Empty	E Occupied	F Free

12	A Cowardly	B Brash	C Confident	D Valiant	E Brave	F Craven

13	A Gather	B Waver	C Muster	D Collect	E Split	F Assemble

14	A Average	B Special	C Mediocre	D Weird	E Mean	F Mode

15	A Ill	B Queasy	C Sick	D Uneasy	E Well	F Sound

EXERCISE 8: Odd Words Out

Instructions: Select TWO words from each group of words that do NOT belong to that group. You are expected to complete this exercise within 5 minutes.

	A	B	C	D	E	F
1	Defector	Traitor	Deserter	Conspirator	Loyalist	Supporter
2	Uneven	Straight	Patchy	Irregular	Variable	Flush
3	Essence	Mist	Gist	Meaning	Point	Dust
4	Workshop	Worship	Respect	Adore	Abode	Admire
5	Guile	Honesty	Deceit	Sincerity	Slyness	Treachery
6	Secure	Affix	Fasten	Clasp	Detach	Isolate
7	Expand	Magnify	Enlarge	Shrink	Reduce	Amplify

8	A Endure	B Climate	C Climax	D Weather	E Survive	F Withstand

9	A Resist	B Defy	C Crumble	D Collapse	E Deteriorate	F Crash

10	A Competition	B Victor	C Champion	D Challenge	E Race	F Tournament

11	A Opinion	B Value	C Premier	D Chief	E Principle	F Belief

12	A Creation	B Making	C Formula	D Formation	E Fencing	F Manufacture

13	A Universal	B Choice	C Generic	D Range	E Common	F Broad

14	A Hurray	B Array	C Assortment	D Sort	E Group	F Collection

15	A Pilot	B Hostess	C Trial	D Test	E Sample	F Compere

Mastering 11+ ™ / English & VR – Book THREE / ashkraft educational

OPPOSITE WORDS

EXERCISE 9: Opposite Words

Instructions: Select the word that has the opposite meaning to the word on the left. There is only one correct answer for each question. Maximum time allowed: 5 minutes

		A	B	C	D	E
1	**COMPOSED**	Flustered	Collected	Serene	Poised	Calm
2	**COMPROMISE**	Negotiate	Concede	Concise	Agreement	Confront
3	**SLOW**	Swift	Sluggish	Gentle	Gradual	Speed
4	**SUAVE**	Charming	Smooth	Polished	Awkward	Dangerous
5	**ADORABLE**	Horrible	Sweet	Dear	Cute	Precious
6	**REBEL**	Objector	Loyalist	Protester	Mutineer	Dissenter
7	**INTEGRAL**	Vital	Important	Immaterial	Essential	Central

    Mastering 11+ ™ / English & VR – Book THREE / ashkraft educational

8	ENLARGE	A Decrease	B Increase	C Broaden	D Expand	E Widen

9	SHARED	A Communal	B Public	C Pooled	D Private	E Common

10	SULKY	A Angry	B Morose	C Cross	D Sullen	E Jovial

11	STUBBORN	A Persistent	B Dogged	C Inflexible	D Tenacious	E Reluctant

12	CONGRATULATE	A Commiserate	B Comment	C Praise	D Cheer	E Applaud

13	LAMENT	A Moan	B Praise	C Sob	D Wail	E Groan

14	RETRACT	A Extent	B Withdraw	C Extend	D Deny	E Rescind

15	JUMPY	A Nervous	B Edgy	C Anxious	D Fidgety	E Calm

EXERCISE 10: Opposite Words

Instructions: Select the word that has the opposite meaning to the word on the left. There is only one correct answer for each question. Maximum allowed: 5 mins

		A	B	C	D	E
1	**GLOOMY**	Shady	Murky	Bright	Opaque	Shadowy

		A	B	C	D	E
2	**RAGS**	Ruins	Bits	Riches	Shreds	Tatters

		A	B	C	D	E
3	**LIABILITY**	Asset	Weakness	Danger	Burden	Liable

		A	B	C	D	E
4	**STARRY**	Dull	Twinkling	Brilliant	Glittery	Shiny

		A	B	C	D	E
5	**WAYWARD**	Naughty	Errant	Defiant	Obedient	Rebellious

		A	B	C	D	E
6	**STEEP**	Excessive	Reasonable	Expensive	Exorbitant	Extreme

		A	B	C	D	E
7	**VEHEMENT**	Passionate	Heated	Violent	Bored	Fervent

Mastering 11+ ™ / English & VR – Book THREE / ashkraft educational

8	VANISH	A Evaporate	B Disappear	C Wane	D Fade	E Appear

9	CONTINUE	A Remain	B Conclude	C Linger	D Stay	E Last

10	DEPARTURE	A Arrival	B Leaving	C Parting	D Retreat	E Exit

11	TAKEN	A Fare	B Free	C Busy	D Full	E Occupied

12	BANNED	A Admitted	B Barred	C Excluded	D Expelled	E Forbidden

13	STRINGENT	A Severe	B Harsh	C Rigid	D Rigorous	E Lax

14	COMPARABLE	A Equivalent	B Akin	C Dissimilar	D Equal	E Like

15	UNITY	A Harmony	B Accord	C Union	D Unanimity	E Disarray

EXERCISE 11: Opposite Words

Instructions: Select the word that has the opposite meaning to the word on the left. There is only one correct answer for each question. Maximum Time: 5 mins

1	BETRAY	A Deceive	B Protect	C Cheat	D Trick	E Dupe

2	INTENSE	A Moderate	B Extreme	C Strong	D Severe	E Deep

3	LIBERTY	A Independence	B Autonomy	C Liberation	D Captivity	E Lively

4	IMPROVE	A Worsen	B Expand	C Increase	D Mend	E Recuperate

5	RECEDE	A Withdraw	B Ebb	C Advance	D Lessen	E Diminish

6	RENOVATE	A Repair	B Damage	C Refurbish	D Mend	E Rewind

7	APPREHENSION	A Confidence	B Angst	C Disquiet	D Concern	E Fear

   Mastering 11+ ™ / English & VR – Book THREE / ashkraft educational

8	FAKE	A Bogus	B Phony	C Replica	D Authentic	E Mock
9	REQUEST	A Plea	B Please	C Need	D Response	E Mandate
10	ASCENT	A Descent	B Climb	C Rise	D Scaling	E Mounting
11	CONCAVE	A Conclude	B Dipped	C Convex	D Hollow	E Dished
12	BENEFIT	A Profit	B Value	C Detriment	D Advantage	E Help
13	BANKRUPT	A Broke	B Solvent	C Bust	D Wrecked	E Spoilt
14	RURAL	A Urban	B Rustic	C Pastoral	D Country	E Bucolic
15	WINTER	A Spring	B Summer	C May	D Twilight	E Fall

EXERCISE 12: Opposite Words

Instructions: Select the word that has the opposite meaning to the word on the left. There is only one correct answer for each question. Maximum Time: 5 minutes

1 PECULIAR	A Truthful	B Strange	C Atypical	D Curious	E Normal

2 LINGERING	A Loitering	B Looting	C Lasting	D Quick	E Persistent

3 FOREIGN	A Alien	B Indigenous	C Remote	D External	E Distant

4 ELEVATE	A Rise	B Lift	C Raise	D Hoist	E Lower

5 COVETED	A Unpopular	B Cowardice	C Desired	D Wanted	E Desirable

6 CURVED	A Bent	B Bowed	C Curled	D Straight	E Rounded

7 COY	A Shy	B Brazen	C Demure	D Modest	E Timid

Mastering 11+ ™ / English & VR – Book THREE / ashkraft educational

8	SOLID	A Hollow	B Dense	C Sealed	D Blocked	E Real

9	DWINDLE	A Fall	B Reduce	C Spread	D Lessen	E Shrink

10	PARDON	A Acquit	B Condemn	C Excuse	D Ignore	E Forgive

11	TIMELY	A Suitable	B Appropriate	C Early	D Sensible	E Apt

12	CONSTRUCT	A Erect	B Assemble	C Form	D Destroy	E Compose

13	DOMINATE	A Dictate	B Meek	C Govern	D Lead	E Rule

14	CONSERVATIVE	A Progressive	B Cautious	C Moderate	D Traditional	E Purist

15	RELIEF	A Help	B Upset	C Reprieve	D Liberation	E Support

EXERCISE 13: Opposite Words

Instructions: Select TWO words from every group of words that are most OPPOSITE to each other in meaning. You are expected to complete this exercise within 5 minutes.

	A	B	C	D	E	F
1	Agree	Approve	Settle	Punish	Disagree	Pardon

	A	B	C	D	E	F
2	Sensible	Match	Practical	Attain	Differ	Reach

	A	B	C	D	E	F
3	Dingy	Smart	Wet	Weird	Heated	Stable

	A	B	C	D	E	F
4	Weak	Week	Brave	Strong	Angry	Solid

	A	B	C	D	E	F
5	Studious	Artistic	Scientific	Statistical	Candid	Careless

	A	B	C	D	E	F
6	March	Tardy	Harsh	Saintly	Mellow	Clean

	A	B	C	D	E	F
7	Habitual	Orbital	Mythical	Factual	Mental	Oval

 Mastering 11+ ™ / English & VR – Book THREE / ashkraft educational

8	A	B	C	D	E	F
	Tall	Dark	Healthy	Sad	Handsome	Ugly

9	A	B	C	D	E	F
	Cruelty	Kindness	Bitter	Lavish	Sprout	Spring

10	A	B	C	D	E	F
	Indicate	Inform	Convict	Appraise	Vindicate	Jovial

11	A	B	C	D	E	F
	Leader	Constant	Variable	Rule	Monarch	Sovereign

12	A	B	C	D	E	F
	Accept	Wage	Dispute	Conduct	Engage	Convey

13	A	B	C	D	E	F
	Regular	Abnormal	Unusual	Irregular	Odd	Peculiar

14	A	B	C	D	E	F
	Thief	Bandit	Capture	Release	Crook	Burglar

15	A	B	C	D	E	F
	Sturdy	Content	Rickety	Glad	Happy	Cheery

EXERCISE 14: Opposite Words

Instructions: Select TWO words from every group of words that are most OPPOSITE to each other in meaning. You are expected to complete this exercise within 5 minutes.

1	A Sluggish	B Roam	C Travel	D Energetic	E Journey	F Stray

2	A Request	B Mild	C Balmy	D Question	E Inquiry	F Probe

3	A Cheeky	B Honest	C Respectful	D Fair	E Sincere	F Frank

4	A Tainted	B Loyal	C Trusty	D Faithful	E Pure	F Reliable

5	A Borrow	B Money	C Bread	D Lend	E Change	F Cash

6	A Rich	B Income	C Expense	D Plush	E Wasteful	F Thrifty

7	A Narrative	B Descriptive	C Literature	D Tragedy	E Poem	F Comedy

Mastering 11+ ™ / English & VR – Book THREE / ashkraft educational

8	A Play	B Pause	C Game	D Resume	E Live	F Relay

9	A Charge	B Straighten	C Trust	D Bend	E Burden	F Concern

10	A Impede	B Facilitate	C Replace	D Surpass	E Succeed	F Displace

11	A Mature	B Undeveloped	C Produce	D Radiate	E Secret	F Emanate

12	A Hole	B Whole	C Cell	D Pit	E Partial	F Hovel

13	A Secrete	B Secret	C Absorb	D Closet	E Stealthy	F Spy

14	A Condemn	B Stable	C Critical	D Attack	E Judge	F Sentence

15	A Rigid	B Failure	C Dud	D Floppy	E Loser	F Lemon

EXERCISE 15: Opposite Words

Instructions: Select TWO words from every group of words that are most OPPOSITE to each other in meaning. You are expected to complete this exercise within 5 minutes.

	A	B	C	D	E	F
1	Preamble	Synopsis	Finale	Abstract	Outline	Summary

	A	B	C	D	E	F
2	Pattern	Condition	Soothing	Irritating	Disorder	Disease

	A	B	C	D	E	F
3	Uniform	Disarray	Uneven	Confusion	Frenzy	Panic

	A	B	C	D	E	F
4	Eager	Keen	Trivial	Crucial	Avid	Ardent

	A	B	C	D	E	F
5	Harmony	Major	Agreement	Accord	Minor	Concord

	A	B	C	D	E	F
6	Excess	Discard	Spare	Keep	Leftover	Waste

	A	B	C	D	E	F
7	Rewind	Relay	Forward	Impact	Send	Stop

Mastering 11+ ™ / English & VR – Book THREE / ashkraft educational

8	A	B	C	D	E	F
	Closed	Narrow	Confine	Reduce	Focus	Open

9	A	B	C	D	E	F
	Dissuade	Teach	Impart	Persuade	Show	Explain

10	A	B	C	D	E	F
	Precede	Drop	Succeed	Tumble	Rumble	Collapse

11	A	B	C	D	E	F
	Life	Vital	Clumsy	Breathe	Agile	Aware

12	A	B	C	D	E	F
	Starve	Famish	Further	Prevent	Thirsty	Farther

13	A	B	C	D	E	F
	Raw	Vintage	Sore	New	Tender	Angry

14	A	B	C	D	E	F
	Royal	Regal	Majestic	Kingly	Mayhem	Order

15	A	B	C	D	E	F
	Abort	Vain	Terminate	Abandon	End	Successful

INCOMPLETE WORDS

EXERCISE 16: Complete the word

Instructions: Complete the word on the right by filling the blank blocks, so that the word formed means the same, as the word on the left.

1 ABANDON

| C | A | N | C | | |

2 TRANQUIL

| S | | E | R | E | | |

3 SHRINK

| D | W | I | | N | D | | |

4 WARFARE

| C | O | N | F | L | | I | | |

5 DELEGATE

| A | S | S | | I | | |

6 ALLOWED

| P | E | R | M | | | T | E | D |

7 PRAY

| M | E | D | | | A | T | E |

8	INSIGHT	V	I	S	I		

9	RADICAL	D	R			T	I	C

10	ERUPT	E	X			O	D	E

11	FIRM	S	T	R	O		

12	SURPLUS	E	X			S	S

13	ANALOGY	P	A	R	A			E	L

14	ODD	W	E	I		

15	INCITE	P	R	O			K	E

Mastering 11+ ™ / English & VR – Book THREE / ashkraft educational

EXERCISE 17: Complete the word

Instructions: Complete the word on the right by filling the blank blocks, so that the word formed means the same, as the word on the left.

| 1 | EXERT | A | P | P | | |

| 2 | ADVENT | S | T | A | | |

| 3 | GUEST | V | I | S | | | O | R |

| 4 | GUST | B | R | | | Z | E |

| 5 | TENTATIVE | U | N | | | R | E |

| 6 | COMPLETE | A | | | L | E |

| 7 | NARROW | S | L | | |

8	LEGEND	C	E	L	E			I	T	Y

9	MAJESTIC	I	M	P	O			N	G

10	WANDER	S	T	R	O		

11	MYRIAD	M			Y

12	COURTEOUS	P	O	L			E	

13	INTERNAL	D	O	M			T	I	C

14	COMPLEX	D	I	F	F			U	L	T

15	RULE	R	E	G	U			T	I	O	N

EXERCISE 18: Complete the word

Instructions: Complete the word on the right by filling the blank blocks, so that the word formed means the same, as the word on the left.

1	SCAM	C	H	E		

2	WEIGHT	B	U	R			N

3	ARROGANT	P	R			D

4	INTELLIGENT	S	M	A		

5	CRUDE	R	O	U		

6	INTRUDER	B	U	R	G	L		

7	CORE	M			N	

8	HORIZONTAL	F			T		

9	SINCERE	H	O	N			T

10	VANE	B	L	A		

11	FOE	R	I	V		

12	HOPE	F	A	I		

13	VERSUS	A	G	A	I	N	

14	BRAVADO	S	H		

15	ELITE	B	E		

Mastering 11+ ™ / English & VR – Book THREE / ashkraft educational

EXERCISE 19: Complete the word

Instructions: Complete the word on the right by filling the blank blocks, so that the word formed means the <u>OPPOSITE</u>, as the word on the left.

| 1 | FACE | | A | V | | | D | |

| 2 | NOISY | | Q | U | I | | | |

| 3 | PURE | | | | P | U | R | E |

| 4 | DANGEROUS | | S | A | | | |

| 5 | ENERGETIC | | S | L | U | | | I | S | H |

| 6 | SQUANDER | | S | A | | | |

| 7 | DISCLOSE | | C | O | N | C | E | | | |

8	STEALTH	H	O	N			T	Y

9	ABSORB	S	E	C	R	E		

10	AGILE	C	L	U	M			

11	SERIOUS	F	U			Y

12	GENTLE	R	O	U		

13	ARTIFICIAL	N	A	T	U	R		

14	EDUCATED			L	I	T	E	R	A	T	E

15	REQUEST	D	E	M	A		

EXERCISE 20: Complete the word

Instructions: Complete the word on the right by filling the blank blocks, so that the word formed means the <u>OPPOSITE</u>, as the word on the left.

1 PRETTY

U		G		

2 VICIOUS

K			D

3 INTENSE

M	O	D	E			T	E

4 SUNLIT

D			K

5 FINITE

		F	I	N	I	T	E

6 PLEASANT

		P	L	E	A	S	A	N	T

7 ALOOF

F		R	I	E	N			Y

8	INSTANT	G	R	A			A	L	

9	PERFECT			P	E	R	F	E	C	T

10	INTENTIONAL	A	C		D	E	N	T	A	L

11	REVEAL	C	O			R

12	PERMANENT	I	N	T			I	M

13	PERIL	S	A	F	E		

14	UNRELIABLE			L	I	A	B	L	E

15	DIM	B	R	I	G			

MATCHING WORDS

EXERCISE 21: Word Matching

Instructions: The table below lists the answers for the questions in this exercise in a random order. Pick the answer based on the word that has similar or closest meaning.

A	B	C	D
Clever	Trust	Check	Liberal

E	F	G	H
Pretty	Petty	Uncertain	Leading

1 INSPECT   A ☐   B ☐   C ☐   D ☐   E ☐   F ☐   G ☐   H ☐

2 AMBIGUOUS   A ☐   B ☐   C ☐   D ☐   E ☐   F ☐   G ☐   H ☐

3 GENEROUS   A ☐   B ☐   C ☐   D ☐   E ☐   F ☐   G ☐   H ☐

4 SMART   A ☐   B ☐   C ☐   D ☐   E ☐   F ☐   G ☐   H ☐

5 TRIVIAL   A ☐   B ☐   C ☐   D ☐   E ☐   F ☐   G ☐   H ☐

6 ATTRACTIVE   A ☐   B ☐   C ☐   D ☐   E ☐   F ☐   G ☐   H ☐

7 BELIEVE   A ☐   B ☐   C ☐   D ☐   E ☐   F ☐   G ☐   H ☐

8 DOMINANT   A ☐   B ☐   C ☐   D ☐   E ☐   F ☐   G ☐   H ☐

EXERCISE 22: Word Matching

Instructions: The table below lists the answers for the questions in this exercise in a random order. Pick the answer based on the word that has similar or closest meaning.

A	B	C	D
Haphazard	Agreeable	Independence	Blunder
E	F	G	H
Exhausted	Knowledge	Thorough	Surprise

1. WISDOM   A ▭   B ▭   C ▭   D ▭   E ▭   F ▭   G ▭   H ▭

2. RANDOM   A ▭   B ▭   C ▭   D ▭   E ▭   F ▭   G ▭   H ▭

3. AUTONOMY   A ▭   B ▭   C ▭   D ▭   E ▭   F ▭   G ▭   H ▭

4. STARTLE   A ▭   B ▭   C ▭   D ▭   E ▭   F ▭   G ▭   H ▭

5. METICULOUS   A ▭   B ▭   C ▭   D ▭   E ▭   F ▭   G ▭   H ▭

6. AMENABLE   A ▭   B ▭   C ▭   D ▭   E ▭   F ▭   G ▭   H ▭

7. STUMBLE   A ▭   B ▭   C ▭   D ▭   E ▭   F ▭   G ▭   H ▭

8. WEARY   A ▭   B ▭   C ▭   D ▭   E ▭   F ▭   G ▭   H ▭

EXERCISE 23: Word Matching

Instructions: The table below lists the answers for the questions in this exercise in a random order. Pick the answer based on the word that has similar or closest meaning.

A	B	C	D
Enchanted	**Offensive**	**Amazing**	**Purpose**
E	F	G	H
Criminal	**Diminish**	**Tyrant**	**Planned**

		A	B	C	D	E	F	G	H
1	SUBSIDE	☐	☐	☐	☐	☐	☐	☐	☐
2	MIRACULOUS	☐	☐	☐	☐	☐	☐	☐	☐
3	DICTATOR	☐	☐	☐	☐	☐	☐	☐	☐
4	MAGICAL	☐	☐	☐	☐	☐	☐	☐	☐
5	OUTLAW	☐	☐	☐	☐	☐	☐	☐	☐
6	OBJECTIONABLE	☐	☐	☐	☐	☐	☐	☐	☐
7	OBJECTIVE	☐	☐	☐	☐	☐	☐	☐	☐
8	CALCULATED	☐	☐	☐	☐	☐	☐	☐	☐

Mastering 11+ ™ / English & VR – Book THREE / ashkraft educational

EXERCISE 24: Word Matching

Instructions: The table below lists the answers for the questions in this exercise in a random order. Pick the answer based on the word that has similar or closest meaning.

A	B	C	D
Punish	Countless	Activate	Lonely
E	F	G	H
Chief	Servant	Trader	Crazy

1	MYRIAD	A	B	C	D	E	F	G	H

2	WACKY	A	B	C	D	E	F	G	H

3	MASTER	A	B	C	D	E	F	G	H

4	DOMESTIC	A	B	C	D	E	F	G	H

5	AVENGE	A	B	C	D	E	F	G	H

6	TRIGGER	A	B	C	D	E	F	G	H

7	SOLITARY	A	B	C	D	E	F	G	H

8	MERCHANT	A	B	C	D	E	F	G	H

EXERCISE 25: Word Matching

Instructions: The table below lists the answers for the questions in this exercise in a random order. Pick the answer based on the word that has similar or closest meaning.

A	B	C	D
Removal	Awful	Scrap	Slice
E	F	G	H
Woodwork	Sharp	Improve	Determined

		A	B	C	D	E	F	G	H
1	PROGRESS	☐	☐	☐	☐	☐	☐	☐	☐
2	WITHDRAWL	☐	☐	☐	☐	☐	☐	☐	☐
3	SHRED	☐	☐	☐	☐	☐	☐	☐	☐
4	JOINERY	☐	☐	☐	☐	☐	☐	☐	☐
5	CARVE	☐	☐	☐	☐	☐	☐	☐	☐
6	JAGGED	☐	☐	☐	☐	☐	☐	☐	☐
7	HEADSTRONG	☐	☐	☐	☐	☐	☐	☐	☐
8	DREADFUL	☐	☐	☐	☐	☐	☐	☐	☐

Mastering 11+ ™ / English & VR – Book THREE / ashkraft educational

EXERCISE 26: Word Matching

Instructions: The table below lists the answers for the questions in this exercise in a random order. Pick the answer based on the word that has similar or closest meaning.

A	B	C	D
Jealous	Keen	Meek	Frown
E	F	G	H
Rework	Whisper	Intrude	Residence

		A	B	C	D	E	F	G	H
1	ZEALOUS	☐	☐	☐	☐	☐	☐	☐	☐
2	BITTER	☐	☐	☐	☐	☐	☐	☐	☐
3	GRIMACE	☐	☐	☐	☐	☐	☐	☐	☐
4	DOMICILE	☐	☐	☐	☐	☐	☐	☐	☐
5	DOCILE	☐	☐	☐	☐	☐	☐	☐	☐
6	REVISE	☐	☐	☐	☐	☐	☐	☐	☐
7	ENCROACH	☐	☐	☐	☐	☐	☐	☐	☐
8	MURMUR	☐	☐	☐	☐	☐	☐	☐	☐

EXERCISE 27: Word Matching

Instructions: The table below lists the answers for the questions in this exercise in a random order. Pick the answer based on the word that has similar or closest meaning.

A	B	C	D
Gathering	Spacious	Occupation	Interfere

E	F	G	H
Obstacle	Gossip	Learner	Forebear

		A	B	C	D	E	F	G	H
1	PROFESSION	☐	☐	☐	☐	☐	☐	☐	☐
2	PUPIL	☐	☐	☐	☐	☐	☐	☐	☐
3	CROWD	☐	☐	☐	☐	☐	☐	☐	☐
4	RUMOUR	☐	☐	☐	☐	☐	☐	☐	☐
5	CAPACIOUS	☐	☐	☐	☐	☐	☐	☐	☐
6	HURDLE	☐	☐	☐	☐	☐	☐	☐	☐
7	TAMPER	☐	☐	☐	☐	☐	☐	☐	☐
8	ANCESTOR	☐	☐	☐	☐	☐	☐	☐	☐

EXERCISE 28: Word Matching

Instructions: The table below lists the answers for the questions in this exercise in a random order. Pick the answer based on the word that has similar or closest meaning.

A	B	C	D
Bloodline	**Musician**	**Strength**	**Passionate**
E	F	G	H
Fortunate	**Organisation**	**Signal**	**Border**

		A	B	C	D	E	F	G	H
1	HERALD	☐	☐	☐	☐	☐	☐	☐	☐
2	PEDIGREE	☐	☐	☐	☐	☐	☐	☐	☐
3	STAMINA	☐	☐	☐	☐	☐	☐	☐	☐
4	INSTITUTE	☐	☐	☐	☐	☐	☐	☐	☐
5	MINSTREL	☐	☐	☐	☐	☐	☐	☐	☐
6	ARDENT	☐	☐	☐	☐	☐	☐	☐	☐
7	AUSPICIOUS	☐	☐	☐	☐	☐	☐	☐	☐
8	HEDGE	☐	☐	☐	☐	☐	☐	☐	☐

EXERCISE 29: Word Matching

Instructions: The table below lists the answers for the questions in this exercise in a random order. Pick the answer based on the word that has similar or closest meaning.

A	B	C	D
Rant	Benefit	View	Fraud
E	F	G	H
Repeat	Prediction	Execute	Encourage

		A	B	C	D	E	F	G	H
1	FORECAST	☐	☐	☐	☐	☐	☐	☐	☐
2	STIMULATE	☐	☐	☐	☐	☐	☐	☐	☐
3	OUTBURST	☐	☐	☐	☐	☐	☐	☐	☐
4	VISTA	☐	☐	☐	☐	☐	☐	☐	☐
5	TRICKSTER	☐	☐	☐	☐	☐	☐	☐	☐
6	ADVANTAGE	☐	☐	☐	☐	☐	☐	☐	☐
7	ITERATE	☐	☐	☐	☐	☐	☐	☐	☐
8	IMPLEMENT	☐	☐	☐	☐	☐	☐	☐	☐

EXERCISE 30: Word Matching

Instructions: The table below lists the answers for the questions in this exercise in a random order. Pick the answer based on the word that has similar or closest meaning.

	A	B	C	D
	Irregular	Rule	Fundamental	Supervise
	E	F	G	H
	Tolerate	Revive	Flustered	Impulsive

#	Word	A	B	C	D	E	F	G	H
1	RESURRECT	☐	☐	☐	☐	☐	☐	☐	☐
2	VITAL	☐	☐	☐	☐	☐	☐	☐	☐
3	CHECKERED	☐	☐	☐	☐	☐	☐	☐	☐
4	SPONTANEOUS	☐	☐	☐	☐	☐	☐	☐	☐
5	GOVERN	☐	☐	☐	☐	☐	☐	☐	☐
6	PRESIDE	☐	☐	☐	☐	☐	☐	☐	☐
7	RATTLED	☐	☐	☐	☐	☐	☐	☐	☐
8	STOMACH	☐	☐	☐	☐	☐	☐	☐	☐

SIMILAR MEANING

EXERCISE 31: Similar Meaning

Instructions: Select TWO words from every group of words that are most SIMILAR to each other in meaning. You are expected to complete this exercise within 5 minutes.

	A	B	C	D	E	F
1	Endure	Perish	Energy	Prevail	Strength	Predominant
2	Shrink	Ship	Export	Expand	Retrieve	Remit
3	Female	Starve	Rich	Stink	Serve	Famish
4	Nature	Character	Nurture	Tender	Cultivate	Imagine
5	Premise	Introduction	Terminal	Synergy	Clarity	Precision
6	Serious	Sway	Fatal	Ring	Straw	Strong
7	Delicious	Feeble	Delicate	Fragrant	Sweet	Spicy

8	A	B	C	D	E	F
	☐	☐	☐	☐	☐	☐
	Vibrant	Town	Vicinity	Urban	Area	People

9	A	B	C	D	E	F
	☐	☐	☐	☐	☐	☐
	Method	Approach	View	March	Rows	Columns

10	A	B	C	D	E	F
	☐	☐	☐	☐	☐	☐
	Content	Volume	Area	Capacity	Capability	Quality

11	A	B	C	D	E	F
	☐	☐	☐	☐	☐	☐
	Minor	Major	Quarter	Half	Full	Main

12	A	B	C	D	E	F
	☐	☐	☐	☐	☐	☐
	Subside	Intelligent	Rage	Fury	Mediate	Turn

13	A	B	C	D	E	F
	☐	☐	☐	☐	☐	☐
	Forever	Each	Always	External	Single	Multiple

14	A	B	C	D	E	F
	☐	☐	☐	☐	☐	☐
	Discipline	Angry	Time	Order	Quick	Lame

15	A	B	C	D	E	F
	☐	☐	☐	☐	☐	☐
	First	Rank	Popular	Failure	Success	Sort

EXERCISE 32: Similar Meaning

Instructions: Select TWO words from every group of words that are most SIMILAR to each other in meaning. You are expected to complete this exercise within 5 minutes.

1

A	B	C	D	E	F
▭	▭	▭	▭	▭	▭
Mercurial	Timid	Lively	Sluggish	Liquid	Metal

2

A	B	C	D	E	F
▭	▭	▭	▭	▭	▭
Play	Stop	Repeat	Forward	Reiterate	Rewind

3

A	B	C	D	E	F
▭	▭	▭	▭	▭	▭
Marsh	Dessert	Forest	Desert	Wave	Fen

4

A	B	C	D	E	F
▭	▭	▭	▭	▭	▭
Tough	Soft	Hard	Meddle	Rich	Stand

5

A	B	C	D	E	F
▭	▭	▭	▭	▭	▭
Scrub	Clean	Dirty	Spine	Spin	Rattle

6

A	B	C	D	E	F
▭	▭	▭	▭	▭	▭
Inaccurate	Correct	Spot	Trigger	Right	Change

7

A	B	C	D	E	F
▭	▭	▭	▭	▭	▭
Internal	External	Interim	Boxed	Temporary	Close

8	**A** ☐ Print	**B** ☐ Prepare	**C** ☐ Destroy	**D** ☐ New	**E** ☐ Old	**F** ☐ Mint

9	**A** ☐ Stamp	**B** ☐ Stash	**C** ☐ Strive	**D** ☐ Stack	**E** ☐ Strong	**F** ☐ Stump

10	**A** ☐ Scholar	**B** ☐ Match	**C** ☐ Design	**D** ☐ Floor	**E** ☐ Plan	**F** ☐ Roof

11	**A** ☐ Essence	**B** ☐ Essential	**C** ☐ Necessary	**D** ☐ Vitamin	**E** ☐ Declare	**F** ☐ Winner

12	**A** ☐ Capacious	**B** ☐ Cramped	**C** ☐ Cradle	**D** ☐ Spacious	**E** ☐ Universe	**F** ☐ Cosmic

13	**A** ☐ Cross	**B** ☐ Careless	**C** ☐ Junction	**D** ☐ Crossroads	**E** ☐ Chopstick	**F** ☐ Linked

14	**A** ☐ Property	**B** ☐ Entity	**C** ☐ Totality	**D** ☐ Diversity	**E** ☐ Nativity	**F** ☐ Entirety

15	**A** ☐ Proactive	**B** ☐ Agile	**C** ☐ Clumsy	**D** ☐ Nimble	**E** ☐ Reactive	**F** ☐ Reciprocate

EXERCISE 33: Similar Meaning

Instructions: Select TWO words from every group of words that are most SIMILAR to each other in meaning. You are expected to complete this exercise within 5 minutes.

	A	B	C	D	E	F
1	Stage	Coach	Mend	Platform	Student	Write

	A	B	C	D	E	F
2	Reader	Author	Librarian	Writer	Books	Student

	A	B	C	D	E	F
3	Miracle	Magician	Witch	Craft	Wonder	Dark

	A	B	C	D	E	F
4	Sensible	Horrible	Delicate	Adventurous	Sensitive	Ardent

	A	B	C	D	E	F
5	Basis	Ground	Biased	Justice	Prejudiced	Values

	A	B	C	D	E	F
6	Numerous	Dozen	Numbers	Humid	Humorous	Hilarious

	A	B	C	D	E	F
7	Tentative	Uneven	Unsure	Provide	Explain	Surety

8	**A** ▭ Various	**B** ▭ Variable	**C** ▭ Vibrant	**D** ▭ Varying	**E** ▭ Vocal	**F** ▭ Exciting

9	**A** ▭ Result	**B** ▭ Proceed	**C** ▭ Check	**D** ▭ Fail	**E** ▭ Verify	**F** ▭ Pass

10	**A** ▭ Arrival	**B** ▭ Depart	**C** ▭ Leave	**D** ▭ Holiday	**E** ▭ Journey	**F** ▭ Airport

11	**A** ▭ Wrangle	**B** ▭ Reconciliation	**C** ▭ Recall	**D** ▭ Express	**E** ▭ Vile	**F** ▭ Quarrel

12	**A** ▭ Perimeter	**B** ▭ Foundation	**C** ▭ Base	**D** ▭ Area	**E** ▭ Rule	**F** ▭ Volume

13	**A** ▭ Forsake	**B** ▭ Forgive	**C** ▭ Abandon	**D** ▭ Forget	**E** ▭ Vacation	**F** ▭ Vocation

14	**A** ▭ Left	**B** ▭ Foregone	**C** ▭ Right	**D** ▭ Evil	**E** ▭ Inevitable	**F** ▭ Envy

15	**A** ▭ Demise	**B** ▭ Despicable	**C** ▭ Dearth	**D** ▭ Shortage	**E** ▭ Derail	**F** ▭ Mount

Mastering 11+ ™ / English & VR – Book THREE / ashkraft educational

EXERCISE 34: Similar Meaning

Instructions: Select TWO words from every group of words that are most SIMILAR to each other in meaning. You are expected to complete this exercise within 5 minutes.

	A	B	C	D	E	F
1	Intervene	Interval	Interfere	Internal	Interim	Intent
2	Rhombus	Crystal	Mine	Diamond	Sharpen	Rack
3	Humble	Maintain	Majestic	Disagree	Loyal	Royal
4	Banish	Exile	Exit	Enter	Dismal	Dismay
5	Vile	Vine	Wine	Whine	Mask	Veil
6	Contain	Extent	Colossus	Milk	Bulk	Hulk
7	Scale	Clamp	Consistency	Stiff	Stability	Agile

8	A Mixer	B Blended	C Mixed	D Unite	E Jumbled	F Jinxed

9	A Private	B Property	C Common	D Shared	E Parking	F Stationery

10	A Author	B Reader	C Recite	D Narrate	E Audience	F Play

11	A Interior	B Decorate	C Demolish	D Diagonal	E Vehement	F Intense

12	A Moderate	B Modern	C Classic	D Chide	E Temperate	F Temperature

13	A Enclosure	B Enclave	C Approve	D Encroach	E Endorse	F Entity

14	A Accept	B Verify	C Object	D Oppose	E Weakness	F Wild

15	A Collection	B Receiver	C Receive	D Collect	E Donate	F Donor

EXERCISE 35: Similar Meaning

Instructions: Select TWO words from every group of words that are most SIMILAR to each other in meaning. You are expected to complete this exercise within 5 minutes.

	A	B	C	D	E	F
1	Beautify	Float	Sink	Decorate	Paint	Brush
2	Shine	Bypass	Dull	Distant	Avoid	Advent
3	Internal	Intent	Intern	Interior	Entire	Encore
4	Steer	Navigate	Run	Walk	Fly	Jump
5	Surround	Surrender	Embed	Survive	Savour	Saviour
6	Naughty	Native	Alien	Innate	Nation	Sea
7	Trespass	Violent	Encroach	Fluent	Respect	Detail

| 8 | A ▭ Yield | B ▭ Retail | C ▭ Roll | D ▭ Rob | E ▭ Hand | F ▭ Surrender |

8	**A** ▭ Yield	**B** ▭ Retail	**C** ▭ Roll	**D** ▭ Rob	**E** ▭ Hand	**F** ▭ Surrender

9	**A** ▭ Object	**B** ▭ Entitle	**C** ▭ Book	**D** ▭ Entity	**E** ▭ Prosper	**F** ▭ Wane

10	**A** ▭ Endure	**B** ▭ Ensure	**C** ▭ Tolerate	**D** ▭ Perish	**E** ▭ Surety	**F** ▭ Enclose

11	**A** ▭ Savour	**B** ▭ Saviour	**C** ▭ Taste	**D** ▭ Entertain	**E** ▭ Boorish	**F** ▭ Salt

12	**A** ▭ Arrive	**B** ▭ Redeem	**C** ▭ Arrest	**D** ▭ Restore	**E** ▭ Redden	**F** ▭ Ridden

13	**A** ▭ Compute	**B** ▭ Callout	**C** ▭ Compensation	**D** ▭ Reward	**E** ▭ Regard	**F** ▭ Damage

14	**A** ▭ Litter	**B** ▭ Accurate	**C** ▭ Loiter	**D** ▭ Loaf	**E** ▭ Charm	**F** ▭ Chaste

15	**A** ▭ Cease	**B** ▭ Stop	**C** ▭ Continue	**D** ▭ Play	**E** ▭ Match	**F** ▭ Dice

ANSWERS

ANSWERS:

EXERCISE 1		EXERCISE 2		EXERCISE 3		EXERCISE 4	
1	B and E	1	B and C	1	B and D	1	C and D
2	E and F	2	B and D	2	D and E	2	A and B
3	B and C	3	B and C	3	C and D	3	A and F
4	E and F	4	C and E	4	A and E	4	C and F
5	C and F	5	B and C	5	E and F	5	C and F
6	D and E	6	E and F	6	D and E	6	B and F
7	A and F	7	A and E	7	E and F	7	C and D
8	C and F	8	D and E	8	B and E	8	B and F
9	E and F	9	C and F	9	B and C	9	A and F
10	B and C	10	A and F	10	D and F	10	B and F
11	A and B	11	A and F	11	B and F	11	B and E
12	C and F	12	A and D	12	E and F	12	A and D
13	B and D	13	C and F	13	B and C	13	B and D
14	E and F	14	A and E	14	B and C	14	C and F
15	C and F	15	A and C	15	A and C	15	B and F

ANSWERS:

	EXERCISE 5		EXERCISE 6		EXERCISE 7		EXERCISE 8
1	B and F	1	A and F	1	A and D	1	E and F
2	C and D	2	D and F	2	A and B	2	B and F
3	E and F	3	C and F	3	D and F	3	B and F
4	A and F	4	B and E	4	B and F	4	A and E
5	B and E	5	D and F	5	B and E	5	B and D
6	C and D	6	C and D	6	C and D	6	E and F
7	A and E	7	A and F	7	A and B	7	D and E
8	E and F	8	A and F	8	C and E	8	B and C
9	A and C	9	E and F	9	A and E	9	A and B
10	B and F	10	E and F	10	B and F	10	B and C
11	A and B	11	C and F	11	B and F	11	C and D
12	B and D	12	B and E	12	A and F	12	C and E
13	A and C	13	A and D	13	B and E	13	B and D
14	E and F	14	D and E	14	B and D	14	A and D
15	B and F	15	A and B	15	E and F	15	B and F

ANSWERS:

EXERCISE 9		EXERCISE 10		EXERCISE 11		EXERCISE 12		EXERCISE 13	
1	A	1	C	1	B	1	E	1	A and E
2	E	2	C	2	A	2	D	2	B and E
3	A	3	A	3	D	3	B	3	A and B
4	D	4	A	4	A	4	E	4	A and D
5	A	5	D	5	C	5	A	5	A and F
6	B	6	B	6	B	6	D	6	C and E
7	C	7	D	7	A	7	B	7	C and D
8	A	8	E	8	D	8	A	8	E and F
9	D	9	B	9	D	9	C	9	A and B
10	E	10	A	10	A	10	B	10	C and E
11	D	11	B	11	C	11	C	11	B and C
12	A	12	A	12	C	12	D	12	A and C
13	B	13	E	13	B	13	B	13	A and D
14	C	14	C	14	A	14	A	14	C and D
15	E	15	E	15	B	15	B	15	A and C

ANSWERS:

EXERCISE 14		EXERCISE 15		EXERCISE 16	
1	A and D	1	A and C	1	EL (CANCEL)
2	B and C	2	C and D	2	NE (SERENE)
3	A and C	3	A and C	3	LE (DWINDLE)
4	A and E	4	C and D	4	CT (CONFLICT)
5	A and D	5	B and E	5	GN (ASSIGN)
6	B and C	6	B and D	6	IT (PERMITTED)
7	D and F	7	A and C	7	IT (MEDITATE)
8	B and D	8	A and F	8	ON (VISION)
9	B and D	9	A and D	9	AS (DRASTIC)
10	A and B	10	A and C	10	PL (EXPLODE)
11	A and B	11	C and E	11	NG (STRONG)
12	B and E	12	C and D	12	CE (EXCESS)
13	A and C	13	B and D	13	LL (PARALLEL)
14	B and C	14	E and F	14	RD (WEIRD)
15	A and D	15	B and F	15	VO (PROVOKE)

ANSWERS:

	EXERCISE 17		EXERCISE 18		EXERCISE 19
1	LY (APPLY)	1	AT (CHEAT)	1	OI (AVOID)
2	RT (START)	2	DE (BURDEN)	2	ET (QUIET)
3	IT (VISITOR)	3	OU (PROUD)	3	IM (IMPURE)
4	EE (BREEZE)	4	RT (SMART)	4	FE (SAFE)
5	SU (UNSURE)	5	GH (ROUGH)	5	GG (SLUGGISH)
6	MP (AMPLE)	6	AR (BURGLAR)	6	VE (SAVE)
7	IM (SLIM)	7	AI (MAIN)	7	AL (CONCEAL)
8	BR (CELEBRITY)	8	LA (FLAT)	8	ES (HONESTY)
9	SI (IMPOSING)	9	ES (HONEST)	9	TE (SECRETE)
10	LL (STROLL)	10	DE (BLADE)	10	SY (CLUMSY)
11	AN (MANY)	11	AL (RIVAL)	11	NN (FUNNY)
12	IT (POLITE)	12	TH (FAITH)	12	GH (ROUGH)
13	ES (DOMESTIC)	13	ST (AGAINST)	13	AL (NATURAL)
14	IC (DIFFICULT)	14	OW (SHOW)	14	IL (ILLITERATE)
15	LA (REGULATION)	15	ST (BEST)	15	ND (DEMAND)

ANSWERS:

EXERCISE 20		EXERCISE 21		EXERCISE 22		EXERCISE 23	
1	LY (UGLY)	1	C	1	F	1	F
2	IN (KIND)	2	G	2	A	2	C
3	RA (MODERATE)	3	D	3	C	3	G
4	AR (DARK)	4	A	4	H	4	A
5	IN (INFINITE)	5	F	5	H	5	E
6	UN (UNPLEASANT)	6	E	6	B	6	B
7	DL (FRIENDLY)	7	B	7	D	7	D
8	DU (GRADUAL)	8	H	8	E	8	H
9	IM (IMPERFECT)						
10	CI (ACCIDENTAL)						
11	VE (COVER)						
12	ER (INTERIM)						
13	TY (SAFETY)						
14	RE (RELIABLE)						
15	HT (BRIGHT)						

ANSWERS:

EXERCISE 24		EXERCISE 25		EXERCISE 26		EXERCISE 27	
1	B	1	G	1	B	1	C
2	H	2	A	2	A	2	G
3	E	3	C	3	D	3	A
4	F	4	E	4	H	4	F
5	A	5	D	5	C	5	B
6	C	6	F	6	E	6	E
7	D	7	H	7	G	7	D
8	G	8	B	8	F	8	H

EXERCISE 28		EXERCISE 29		EXERCISE 30	
1	G	1	F	1	F
2	A	2	H	2	C
3	C	3	A	3	A
4	F	4	C	4	H
5	B	5	D	5	B
6	D	6	B	6	D
7	E	7	E	7	G
8	H	8	G	8	E

ANSWERS:

	EXERCISE 31		EXERCISE 32		EXERCISE 33
1	A and D	1	A and C	1	A and D
2	B and C	2	C and E	2	B and D
3	B and F	3	A and F	3	A and E
4	C and E	4	A and C	4	C and E
5	E and F	5	A and B	5	C and E
6	A and C	6	B and E	6	E and F
7	B and C	7	C and E	7	A and C
8	C and E	8	D and F	8	C and F
9	A and B	9	B and D	9	C and E
10	B and D	10	C and E	10	B and C
11	B and F	11	B and C	11	A and F
12	C and D	12	A and D	12	B and C
13	A and C	13	C and D	13	A and C
14	A and D	14	C and F	14	B and E
15	B and F	15	B and D	15	C and D

ANSWERS:

EXERCISE 34			EXERCISE 35	
1	A and C		1	A and D
2	A and D		2	B and E
3	C and F		3	A and D
4	A and B		4	A and B
5	E and F		5	A and C
6	C and F		6	B and D
7	C and E		7	A and C
8	B and C		8	A and F
9	C and D		9	A and D
10	C and D		10	A and C
11	E and F		11	A and C
12	A and E		12	B and D
13	C and E		13	C and D
14	C and D		14	C and D
15	C and D		15	A and B

Email enquiry@mastering11plus.com if you need any clarification on the answers.

Progress Chart

Exercise	Attempt 1 Date	Score	Attempt 2 Date	Score
1. Odd words				
2. Odd Words				
3. Odd Words				
4. Odd Words				
5. Odd Words				
6. Odd Words				
7. Odd Words				
8. Odd Words				
9. Antonyms				
10. Antonyms				
11. Antonyms				
12. Antonyms				
13. Antonyms				
14. Antonyms				
15. Antonyms				

Exercise	Attempt 1 Date	Score	Attempt 2 Date	Score
16. Complete the word				
17. Complete the word				
18. Complete the word				
19. Complete the word				
20. Complete the word				
21. Word Matching				
22. Word Matching				
23. Word Matching				
24. Word Matching				
25. Word Matching				
26. Word Matching				
27. Word Matching				
28. Word Matching				
29. Word Matching				
30. Word Matching				
31. Synonyms				
32. Synonyms				
33. Synonyms				
34. Synonyms				
35. Synonyms				

Other books in the Mastering 11+ series:

- ➢ English & Verbal Reasoning – Practice Book 1
- ➢ English & Verbal Reasoning – Practice Book 2

- ➢ Cloze Tests – Practice Book 1
- ➢ Cloze Tests – Practice Book 2
- ➢ Cloze Tests – Practice Book 3

- ➢ Maths – Practice Book 1
- ➢ Maths – Practice Book 2
- ➢ Maths – Practice Book 3

- ➢ Comprehension – Multiple Choice Exercise Book 1
- ➢ Comprehension – Multiple Choice Exercise Book 2
- ➢ Comprehension – Multiple Choice Exercise Book 3

- ➢ CEM Practice Papers – Pack 1
- ➢ CEM Practice Papers – Pack 2
- ➢ CEM Practice Papers – Pack 3
- ➢ CEM Practice Papers – Pack 4

All queries to **enquiry@mastering11plus.com**

Printed in Great Britain
by Amazon